WORDS OF WISDOM

A PLAN FOR SUCCESS
BY MARILYN BOYER

Character Concepts

RUSTBURG, VIRGINIA

Words of Wisdom • A Plan for Success

Copyright © 2011, 2013 by Marilyn Boyer

ALL RIGHTS RESERVED

First printing 2011
Second printing 2013

editing and graphic design by Mary Ann Edman

ISBN: 978-0-9777685-7-8

Published by The Learning Parent
2430 Sunnymeade Road
Rustburg, VA 24588
www.CharacterConcepts.com

Proudly printed in the United States of America

www.thelearningparent.com

PHOTO CREDITS

Except as listed below, all photos were acquired from Stock.XCHNG. We are grateful to this
site for its excellent quality photographs and generous free downloads.

Photos from Clipart.com: 21

Photos from MorgueFile.com: 11, 13, 14, 25, 27, 31, 37, 40, 42, 68, 69, 89, 98, 125, 127, 128, 130,
134, 139, 148, 151, 158, 159, 160, 161, 162, 163, 178, 179, 180, 181, 184, 185, 191

193: black-footed albatross: http://ocean.nationalgeographic.com/ocean/photos/sea-
birds/#/sea-birds03-albatross_18250_600x450.jpg

195: http://ocean.nationalgeographic.com/ocean/photos/deep-sea-creatures/#/deep-
sea04-fangtooth_18164_600x450.jpg

Photos from various public domain sources: 30, 38, 73, 79, 116, 117, 118

Photos by Mary Ann Edman: 53, 109, 112, 114, 115, 177, front cover photo

WORDS OF WISDOM

A PLAN FOR SUCCESS
BY MARILYN BOYER

Appropriate for junior high and high school
Designed for use with THE WORDS OF MY MOUTH FLASHCARD SET

RUSTBURG, VIRGINIA

INTRODUCTION

Our words can be life-giving words, or they can be used as arrows to pierce and wound others. God has much to say in His Word on the use of our words.

Matthew 12:37 tells us,

"For by thy words thou shalt be justified, and by thy words thou shalt be condemned."

If we learn to properly use our words, God will make a way for us. He will bring us opportunities we might not otherwise have.

Proverbs 22:11 tells us,

"He who loves purity of heart and whose speech is gracious, the king is his friend."

We will have to use words our whole life and that is why God gives us so much input about the use of our words in His Word. Learn His wisdom and watch Him work out great opportunities in your life!

WORDS SCRIPTURE USES TO REFER TO OUR WORDS:

Words

Lips

Tongue

Mouth

INSTRUCTIONS FOR USE

This study is designed to help you determine to practically put into use insights you gain from Scripture about the use of your words. If you can get a glimpse of the importance of your choice of words and learn to speak intentionally, you will be much more likely to be a profitable servant of God and He will make opportunities for you that are not available to those who have not gotten a grasp of the eternal importance of the words of our mouth in everyday life. I hope this study will prove to be a blessing to you in ways you had never even considered. Be sure to "hide God's Word in your heart" as you work through it.

This practical study is designed very simply. It won't take long each day to complete. Each page has one verse and three exercises to complete. You only need to complete one page per day. Here's how to do it:

- First of all, simply write the verse on the lines provided. ex., *Proverbs 16:24, "Pleasant words are as an honeycomb, sweet to the soul, and health to the bones."* You can use whatever version of the Bible you choose.

- Next, record an insight you can learn from this verse. ex., *Pleasant words are sweet to hear (both to the giver of the words and the receiver of the words) and even can help to bring healing to my body. (That's pretty powerful!)*

- Lastly, either rewrite the verse, personalizing it as you do, ex., *Pleasant words are like a honeycomb, sweet to my soul and health to my bones.*

- OR, turn it into a prayer. ex., *Lord, help me to purpose to use pleasant words. They not only have a good effect on others, but will affect my own body in a positive way. My words are powerful! Help me to use that power wisely.*

- OR, purpose a specific step of action to help you practically implement this. ex., *Lord, my younger sister looks up to me. Sometimes she can be irritating, but Lord, help me to purposely speak only words that will encourage her and not make her feel bad.*

- OR think of a person in real life or Scripture who is a good example of speaking pleasant words. ex., *Mrs. Cooper almost always says something to encourage me when I see her in church. My day always seems to feel a bit brighter after seeing her in church.*

Also you have a pack of Scripture verses, *Words of My Mouth Scripture Memory Flashcards,* that comes with this curriculum package. Each day, take a few minutes to work on learning these verses. Work on one at a time until you have committed it to memory. (The goal is to actually learn them and meditate on what they say, not to work through the pack in record speed, but to let them become a part of the way you think.) Then begin working on the next verse, taking a few minutes to review ones previously learned. By the time you get through the pack you will have a great arsenal of verses that will guide you in times of temptation to make wise word choices.

May you learn to honor God in everyday life and it is my prayer that He will use you to accomplish great and mighty purposes!

—Marilyn

TABLE OF CONTENTS

WORDS

LIPS

TONGUE

TABLE OF CONTENTS continued

MOUTH

WORDS

WORDS OF WISDOM

ACCEPTABLE WORDS

Ecclesiastes 12:10

verse
_____
_____
_____
_____
_____

insight learned:
_____
_____
_____
_____
_____
_____

personalized verse, prayer, or specific project:
_____
_____
_____
_____
_____
_____
_____
_____
_____
_____
_____

∞∞ BITTER WORDS ∞∞

Psalm 64:3

verse

_____
_____
_____
_____
_____

insight learned:

_____
_____
_____
_____
_____
_____

personalized verse, prayer, or specific project:

_____
_____
_____
_____
_____
_____
_____
_____
_____
_____

⚬⚬⚬ BLASPHEMOUS WORDS ⚬⚬⚬
Colossians 3:8

verse

_____
_____
_____
_____
_____

insight learned:

_____
_____
_____
_____
_____
_____

personalized verse, prayer, or specific project:

_____
_____
_____
_____
_____
_____
_____
_____
_____
_____

∽ BOLD WORDS ∽
Acts 4:31

verse

_____
_____
_____
_____
_____

insight learned:

_____
_____
_____
_____
_____

personalized verse, prayer, or specific project:

_____
_____
_____
_____
_____
_____
_____
_____
_____
_____

~~~~ BOLD WORDS ~~~~
Philippians 1:14

verse

_____

_____

_____

_____

insight learned:

_____

_____

_____

_____

_____

personalized verse, prayer, or specific project:

_____

_____

_____

_____

_____

_____

_____

_____

_____

_____

∞∞ BREAKING WORDS ∞∞
Job 19:2

verse

_____
_____
_____
_____
_____

insight learned:

_____
_____
_____
_____
_____
_____

personalized verse, prayer, or specific project:

_____
_____
_____
_____
_____
_____
_____
_____
_____
_____

∽ BY YOUR WORDS . . . ∽
Matthew 12:37

verse

_____
_____
_____
_____
_____

insight learned:

_____
_____
_____
_____
_____
_____

personalized verse, prayer, or specific project:

_____
_____
_____
_____
_____
_____
_____
_____
_____

∞ COMFORTING WORDS ∞
I Thessalonians 4:18

verse

_____
_____
_____
_____
_____

insight learned:

_____
_____
_____
_____
_____
_____

personalized verse, prayer, or specific project:

_____
_____
_____
_____
_____
_____
_____
_____
_____
_____

∽ CONTENTIOUS WORDS ∽
Proverbs 18:6

verse

_____
_____
_____
_____
_____

insight learned:

_____
_____
_____
_____
_____
_____

personalized verse, prayer, or specific project:

_____
_____
_____
_____
_____
_____
_____
_____
_____
_____
_____

⌁ CORRUPT WORDS ⌁

Daniel 2:9

verse

_____
_____
_____
_____
_____

insight learned:

_____
_____
_____
_____
_____
_____

personalized verse, prayer, or specific project:

_____
_____
_____
_____
_____
_____
_____
_____
_____
_____
_____

∼ DEVOURING WORDS ∼
Psalm 52:4

verse

_____
_____
_____
_____
_____

insight learned:

_____
_____
_____
_____
_____
_____

personalized verse, prayer, or specific project:

_____
_____
_____
_____
_____
_____
_____
_____
_____
_____

~ EATING WORDS ~

II Timothy 2:17

verse

_____
_____
_____
_____
_____

insight learned:

_____
_____
_____
_____
_____
_____

personalized verse, prayer, or specific project:

_____
_____
_____
_____
_____
_____
_____
_____
_____
_____
_____

∽ ENSNARING WORDS ∽
Proverbs 6:2

verse

_____
_____
_____
_____
_____

insight learned:

_____
_____
_____
_____
_____
_____

personalized verse, prayer, or specific project:

_____
_____
_____
_____
_____
_____
_____
_____
_____
_____
_____

~ ENTICING WORDS ~
I Corinthians 2:4

verse

_____
_____
_____
_____
_____

insight learned:

_____
_____
_____
_____
_____
_____

personalized verse, prayer, or specific project:

_____
_____
_____
_____
_____
_____
_____
_____
_____
_____
_____
_____

⟡ EXHORTING WORDS ⟡
Acts 13:15, 15:32

verse

_____
_____
_____
_____
_____

insight learned:

_____
_____
_____
_____
_____
_____

personalized verse, prayer, or specific project:

_____
_____
_____
_____
_____
_____
_____
_____
_____
_____

Words of Wisdom

✠ FAITHFUL WORDS ✠

Titus 1:9

verse

_____

_____

_____

_____

_____

insight learned:

_____

_____

_____

_____

_____

_____

personalized verse, prayer, or specific project:

_____

_____

_____

_____

_____

_____

_____

_____

_____

_____

_____

_____

FEIGNED WORDS

II Peter 2:3

verse

_____
_____
_____
_____
_____

insight learned:

_____
_____
_____
_____
_____
_____

personalized verse, prayer, or specific project:

_____
_____
_____
_____
_____
_____
_____
_____
_____
_____
_____

⌘ FEW WORDS ⌘

Acts 24:4

verse

_____
_____
_____
_____
_____

insight learned:

_____
_____
_____
_____
_____
_____

personalized verse, prayer, or specific project:

_____
_____
_____
_____
_____
_____
_____
_____
_____
_____
_____
_____
_____

⌇⌇ FEW WORDS ⌇⌇
Ecclesiastes 5:2

verse

_____
_____
_____
_____
_____

insight learned:

_____
_____
_____
_____
_____

personalized verse, prayer, or specific project:

_____
_____
_____
_____
_____
_____
_____
_____
_____

Words of Wisdom

~ FITLY SPOKEN WORDS ~
Proverbs 25:11

verse

_____
_____
_____
_____
_____

insight learned:

_____
_____
_____
_____
_____

personalized verse, prayer, or specific project:

_____
_____
_____
_____
_____
_____
_____
_____
_____
_____

⠶ FLATTERING WORDS ⠶
Proverbs 2:16, 7:5

verse

_____
_____
_____
_____
_____

insight learned:

_____
_____
_____
_____
_____
_____

personalized verse, prayer, or specific project:

_____
_____
_____
_____
_____
_____
_____
_____
_____
_____
_____
_____

⌒⌒ FLATTERING WORDS ⌒⌒
I Thessalonians 2:5

verse

_____
_____
_____
_____
_____

insight learned:

_____
_____
_____
_____
_____
_____

personalized verse, prayer, or specific project:

_____
_____
_____
_____
_____
_____
_____
_____
_____
_____
_____
_____

~∞∞ FOOLISH WORDS ∞∞~
Proverbs 14:3, 15:14

verse

_____
_____
_____
_____
_____

insight learned:

_____
_____
_____
_____
_____
_____

personalized verse, prayer, or specific project:

_____
_____
_____
_____
_____
_____
_____
_____

⚬⚬ FRUITFUL WORDS ⚬⚬
Proverbs 12:14, 13:2

verse

_____
_____
_____
_____
_____

insight learned:

_____
_____
_____
_____
_____

personalized verse, prayer, or specific project:

_____
_____
_____
_____
_____
_____
_____
_____
_____
_____

⚬⟭ FULL OF WORDS ⟬⚬
Ecclesiastes 10:14

verse

_____

_____

_____

_____

_____

insight learned:

_____

_____

_____

_____

_____

personalized verse, prayer, or specific project:

_____

_____

_____

_____

_____

_____

_____

_____

_____

_____

∾ GOOD WORDS ∾
Proverbs 12:25

verse

_____
_____
_____
_____
_____

insight learned:

_____
_____
_____
_____
_____

personalized verse, prayer, or specific project:

_____
_____
_____
_____
_____
_____
_____
_____
_____
_____

⊶⧜⊷ GRACIOUS WORDS ⧜⊷

Luke 4:22

verse

_____
_____
_____
_____
_____

insight learned:

_____
_____
_____
_____
_____

personalized verse, prayer, or specific project:

_____
_____
_____
_____
_____
_____
_____
_____
_____

⚬⚬⚬ GRIEVOUS WORDS ⚬⚬⚬
Proverbs 15:1

verse

_____
_____
_____
_____
_____

insight learned:

_____
_____
_____
_____
_____
_____

personalized verse, prayer, or specific project:

_____
_____
_____
_____
_____
_____
_____
_____
_____
_____

⟋⟍ GUILELESS WORDS ⟋⟍

I Peter 2:22

verse

_____
_____
_____
_____
_____

insight learned:

_____
_____
_____
_____
_____
_____

personalized verse, prayer, or specific project:

_____
_____
_____
_____
_____
_____
_____
_____
_____
_____

⠶⠶ HASTY WORDS ⠶⠶
Proverbs 29:20

verse

_____
_____
_____
_____

insight learned:

_____
_____
_____
_____
_____

personalized verse, prayer, or specific project:

_____
_____
_____
_____
_____
_____
_____
_____
_____
_____

∾ IDLE WORDS ∾
Matthew 12:36

verse

_____

_____

_____

_____

_____

insight learned:

_____

_____

_____

_____

_____

_____

personalized verse, prayer, or specific project:

_____

_____

_____

_____

_____

_____

_____

_____

ᴓᴓ JOYFUL WORDS ᴓᴓ
Proverbs 15:23

verse

_____
_____
_____
_____
_____

insight learned:

_____
_____
_____
_____
_____

personalized verse, prayer, or specific project:

_____
_____
_____
_____
_____
_____
_____
_____
_____
_____
_____
_____

⸙ LIFE-GIVING WORDS ⸙
Proverbs 15:4

verse

_____
_____
_____
_____
_____

insight learned:

_____
_____
_____
_____
_____
_____

personalized verse, prayer, or specific project:

_____
_____
_____
_____
_____
_____
_____
_____
_____
_____

⟳ LYING WORDS ⟳
Isaiah 32:7

verse

_____
_____
_____
_____
_____

insight learned:

_____
_____
_____
_____
_____

personalized verse, prayer, or specific project:

_____
_____
_____
_____
_____
_____
_____
_____
_____
_____
_____

∞ MALICIOUS WORDS ∞
III John 10

verse

_____
_____
_____
_____
_____

insight learned:

_____
_____
_____
_____
_____
_____

personalized verse, prayer, or specific project:

_____
_____
_____
_____
_____
_____
_____
_____
_____
_____

⸙⸙ MANY WORDS ⸙⸙
Ecclesiastes 5:7

verse

_____
_____
_____
_____
_____

insight learned:

_____
_____
_____
_____
_____
_____

personalized verse, prayer, or specific project:

_____
_____
_____
_____
_____
_____
_____
_____
_____
_____
_____

MULTITUDE OF WORDS

Ecclesiastes 5:3; Job 11:2

verse

_____
_____
_____
_____
_____

insight learned:

_____
_____
_____
_____
_____

personalized verse, prayer, or specific project:

_____
_____
_____
_____
_____
_____
_____
_____
_____
_____
_____

∞ OFFENSIVE WORDS ∞

James 3:2

verse

_____
_____
_____
_____
_____

insight learned:

_____
_____
_____
_____
_____
_____

personalized verse, prayer, or specific project:

_____
_____
_____
_____
_____
_____
_____
_____
_____
_____

∾ PLEASANT WORDS ∾
Proverbs 16:24

verse

_____
_____
_____
_____
_____

insight learned:

_____
_____
_____
_____
_____

personalized verse, prayer, or specific project:

_____
_____
_____
_____
_____
_____
_____
_____
_____

∞ PROUD WORDS ∞
Proverbs 14:3

verse

_____

_____

_____

_____

_____

insight learned:

_____

_____

_____

_____

_____

personalized verse, prayer, or specific project:

_____

_____

_____

_____

_____

_____

_____

_____

_____

_____

⚬ꝏ PURE WORDS ꝏ⚬

Proverbs 15:26

verse

_____
_____
_____
_____
_____

insight learned:

_____
_____
_____
_____
_____
_____

personalized verse, prayer, or specific project:

_____
_____
_____
_____
_____
_____
_____
_____
_____
_____
_____

·∞· PURSUING WORDS ·∞·

Proverbs 19:7

verse

_____
_____
_____
_____
_____

insight learned:

_____
_____
_____
_____
_____

personalized verse, prayer, or specific project:

_____
_____
_____
_____
_____
_____
_____
_____
_____
_____

·∞ RASH WORDS ∞·
Ecclesiastes 5:2

verse

_____

_____

_____

_____

_____

insight learned:

_____

_____

_____

_____

_____

personalized verse, prayer, or specific project:

_____

_____

_____

_____

_____

_____

_____

_____

_____

_____

_____

∼∞ RIGHT WORDS ∞∼
Proverbs 8:6

verse

_____
_____
_____
_____
_____

insight learned:

_____
_____
_____
_____
_____
_____

personalized verse, prayer, or specific project:

_____
_____
_____
_____
_____
_____
_____
_____
_____
_____
_____

⚮ RIGHTLY DIVIDED WORDS ⚮
II Timothy 2:15

verse

_____
_____
_____
_____
_____

insight learned:

_____
_____
_____
_____
_____
_____

personalized verse, prayer, or specific project:

_____
_____
_____
_____
_____
_____
_____
_____
_____
_____

∞∞ SKILLFUL WORDS ∞∞
Hebrews 5:13

verse

_____
_____
_____
_____
_____

insight learned:

_____
_____
_____
_____
_____

personalized verse, prayer, or specific project:

_____
_____
_____
_____
_____
_____
_____
_____
_____

⋘ SOFT WORDS ⋙
Proverbs 15:1

verse

_____
_____
_____
_____
_____

insight learned:

_____
_____
_____
_____
_____

personalized verse, prayer, or specific project:

_____
_____
_____
_____
_____
_____
_____
_____
_____
_____

∞ SOFT WORDS ∞
Psalm 55:21

verse

_____

_____

_____

_____

_____

insight learned:

_____

_____

_____

_____

_____

_____

personalized verse, prayer, or specific project:

_____

_____

_____

_____

_____

_____

_____

_____

_____

_____

_____

∽🐚 SOUND WORDS 🐚∾
II Timothy 1:13

verse

_____
_____
_____
_____

insight learned:

_____
_____
_____
_____
_____

personalized verse, prayer, or specific project:

_____
_____
_____
_____
_____
_____
_____
_____
_____

∽✺ SPARING WORDS ✺∽
Proverbs 17:27

verse

_____
_____
_____
_____
_____

insight learned:

_____
_____
_____
_____
_____
_____

personalized verse, prayer, or specific project:

_____
_____
_____
_____
_____
_____
_____
_____
_____
_____
_____

◦◦◦ SWEET WORDS ◦◦◦
Proverbs 23:8

verse

_____

_____

_____

_____

_____

insight learned:

_____

_____

_____

_____

_____

_____

personalized verse, prayer, or specific project:

_____

_____

_____

_____

_____

_____

_____

_____

_____

_____

~ TIMELY WORDS ~

II Timothy 4:2

verse

_____
_____
_____
_____
_____

insight learned:

_____
_____
_____
_____
_____

personalized verse, prayer, or specific project:

_____
_____
_____
_____
_____
_____
_____
_____
_____
_____
_____

∼∾∽ TOO MANY WORDS ∼∾∽

Proverbs 10:19

verse

_____
_____
_____
_____
_____

insight learned:

_____
_____
_____
_____
_____
_____

personalized verse, prayer, or specific project:

_____
_____
_____
_____
_____
_____
_____
_____
_____
_____

∞∞ TRANSGRESSING WORDS ∞∞
Proverbs 22:12

verse

_____

_____

_____

_____

_____

insight learned:

_____

_____

_____

_____

_____

_____

personalized verse, prayer, or specific project:

_____

_____

_____

_____

_____

_____

_____

_____

_____

_____

TROUBLING WORDS
II Thessalonians 2:2

verse

_____
_____
_____
_____
_____

insight learned:

_____
_____
_____
_____
_____
_____

personalized verse, prayer, or specific project:

_____
_____
_____
_____
_____
_____
_____
_____
_____
_____
_____

⚉ TRUTHFUL WORDS ⚉

Psalm 119:43

verse

_____
_____
_____
_____

insight learned:

_____
_____
_____
_____
_____
_____

personalized verse, prayer, or specific project:

_____
_____
_____
_____
_____
_____
_____
_____
_____
_____
_____

~UNDERSTANDING WORDS ~
Proverbs 2:6

verse

_____
_____
_____
_____
_____

insight learned:

_____
_____
_____
_____
_____
_____

personalized verse, prayer, or specific project:

_____
_____
_____
_____
_____
_____
_____
_____
_____
_____

∞ UPRIGHT WORDS ∞
Proverbs 12:6

verse

_____

_____

_____

_____

_____

insight learned:

_____

_____

_____

_____

_____

personalized verse, prayer, or specific project:

_____

_____

_____

_____

_____

_____

_____

_____

_____

∾∾ VAIN WORDS ∾∾
Ephesians 5:6

verse

_____
_____
_____
_____
_____

insight learned:

_____
_____
_____
_____
_____

personalized verse, prayer, or specific project:

_____
_____
_____
_____
_____
_____
_____
_____
_____
_____

~~~ VAIN WORDS ~~~
Job 16:3

verse

_____
_____
_____
_____
_____

insight learned:

_____
_____
_____
_____
_____
_____

personalized verse, prayer, or specific project:

_____
_____
_____
_____
_____
_____
_____
_____
_____
_____
_____
_____

∾ WHOLESOME WORDS ∾
I Timothy 6:3

verse

_____
_____
_____
_____
_____

insight learned:

_____
_____
_____
_____
_____
_____

personalized verse, prayer, or specific project:

_____
_____
_____
_____
_____
_____
_____
_____
_____
_____
_____
_____

☙ WICKED WORDS ❧
Proverbs 12:6

verse

_____
_____
_____
_____
_____

insight learned:

_____
_____
_____
_____
_____
_____

personalized verse, prayer, or specific project:

_____
_____
_____
_____
_____
_____
_____
_____
_____
_____
_____
_____

⚮ WISE WORDS ⚮

Ecclesiastes 9:17; 10:12; 12:11

verse

_____
_____
_____
_____
_____

insight learned:

_____
_____
_____
_____
_____
_____

personalized verse, prayer, or specific project:

_____
_____
_____
_____
_____
_____
_____
_____
_____
_____

∽∽∽ WISE WORDS ∽∽∽
Proverbs 1:6

verse

_____
_____
_____
_____
_____

insight learned:

_____
_____
_____
_____
_____

personalized verse, prayer, or specific project:

_____
_____
_____
_____
_____
_____
_____
_____
_____
_____

⠦⠶ WORDS OF FAITH ⠶⠦
I Timothy 4:6

verse

_____
_____
_____
_____
_____

insight learned:

_____
_____
_____
_____
_____

personalized verse, prayer, or specific project:

_____
_____
_____
_____
_____
_____
_____
_____
_____
_____

⤳ WORDS SPOKEN IN DUE SEASON ⤳
Proverbs 15:23

verse

_____
_____
_____
_____
_____

insight learned:

_____
_____
_____
_____
_____
_____

personalized verse, prayer, or specific project:

_____
_____
_____
_____
_____
_____
_____
_____
_____

✺ WORDS OF STRIFE ✺
II Timothy 2:14

verse

_____
_____
_____
_____
_____

insight learned:

_____
_____
_____
_____
_____
_____

personalized verse, prayer, or specific project:

_____
_____
_____
_____
_____
_____
_____
_____
_____
_____
_____
_____

∾ WORDS OF TESTIMONY ∾

I Timothy 4:12

verse

_____

_____

_____

_____

_____

insight learned:

_____

_____

_____

_____

_____

_____

personalized verse, prayer, or specific project:

_____

_____

_____

_____

_____

_____

_____

_____

_____

_____

∞ WORDS OF TRUTH ∞

Proverbs 22:21, 23:12

verse

_____

_____

_____

_____

_____

insight learned:

_____

_____

_____

_____

_____

personalized verse, prayer, or specific project:

_____

_____

_____

_____

_____

_____

_____

_____

_____

☙ WORLDLY WORDS ☙
1 Corinthians 2:13

verse

_____
_____
_____
_____
_____

insight learned:

_____
_____
_____
_____
_____

personalized verse, prayer, or specific project:

_____
_____
_____
_____
_____
_____
_____
_____
_____
_____
_____

∞ WOUNDING WORDS ∞
Proverbs 18:8; 26:22

verse

_____

_____

_____

_____

_____

insight learned:

_____

_____

_____

_____

_____

personalized verse, prayer, or specific project:

_____

_____

_____

_____

_____

_____

_____

_____

_____

WORDS OF WISDOM

⁓ BURNING LIPS ⁓

Proverbs 16:27

verse

_____
_____
_____
_____
_____

insight learned:

_____
_____
_____
_____
_____
_____

personalized verse, prayer, or specific project:

_____
_____
_____
_____
_____
_____
_____
_____
_____
_____
_____
_____

⚬⚬⚬ DESTRUCTIVE LIPS ⚬⚬⚬
Proverbs 13:3

verse

_____
_____
_____
_____
_____

insight learned:

_____
_____
_____
_____
_____
_____

personalized verse, prayer, or specific project:

_____
_____
_____
_____
_____
_____
_____
_____
_____
_____
_____

∽∾ DISHONORING LIPS ∾∽
Romans 2:23

verse

_____
_____
_____
_____
_____

insight learned:

_____
_____
_____
_____
_____
_____

personalized verse, prayer, or specific project:

_____
_____
_____
_____
_____
_____
_____
_____
_____
_____

GRACEFUL LIPS

Proverbs 22:11

verse

_____

_____

_____

_____

_____

insight learned:

_____

_____

_____

_____

_____

_____

personalized verse, prayer, or specific project:

_____

_____

_____

_____

_____

_____

_____

_____

_____

_____

⟪⟫ HONORING LIPS ⟪⟫
Matthew 15:8

verse

_____

_____

_____

_____

_____

insight learned:

_____

_____

_____

_____

_____

personalized verse, prayer, or specific project:

_____

_____

_____

_____

_____

_____

_____

_____

_____

∞ INDIGNANT LIPS ∞

Isaiah 30:27

verse

_____
_____
_____
_____
_____

insight learned:

_____
_____
_____
_____
_____
_____

personalized verse, prayer, or specific project:

_____
_____
_____
_____
_____
_____
_____
_____
_____
_____
_____

∽∽ LYING LIPS ∽∽
Proverbs 10:18

verse

_____
_____
_____
_____
_____

insight learned:

_____
_____
_____
_____
_____
_____

personalized verse, prayer, or specific project:

_____
_____
_____
_____
_____
_____
_____
_____
_____
_____
_____

☙ POISONOUS LIPS ❧

Romans 3:13

verse

_____
_____
_____
_____
_____

insight learned:

_____
_____
_____
_____
_____
_____

personalized verse, prayer, or specific project:

_____
_____
_____
_____
_____
_____
_____
_____
_____

⚬⚬⚬ REFRAINED LIPS ⚬⚬⚬
Proverbs 10:19

verse

_____

_____

_____

_____

insight learned:

_____

_____

_____

_____

_____

personalized verse, prayer, or specific project:

_____

_____

_____

_____

_____

_____

_____

_____

_____

_____

_____

∞ RIGHTEOUS LIPS ∞

Proverbs 10:21, 10:32

verse

_____

_____

_____

_____

_____

insight learned:

_____

_____

_____

_____

_____

_____

personalized verse, prayer, or specific project:

_____

_____

_____

_____

_____

_____

_____

_____

_____

_____

THANKFUL LIPS

Hebrews 13:15

verse

_____

_____

_____

_____

_____

insight learned:

_____

_____

_____

_____

_____

personalized verse, prayer, or specific project:

_____

_____

_____

_____

_____

_____

_____

_____

∞ UNCLEAN LIPS ∞
Isaiah 6:5

verse

_____
_____
_____
_____
_____

insight learned:

_____
_____
_____
_____
_____

personalized verse, prayer, or specific project:

_____
_____
_____
_____
_____
_____
_____
_____
_____
_____
_____

TONGUE

WORDS OF WISDOM

⟬⟬ BACKBITING TONGUE ⟬⟬
Psalm 15:3

verse

_____
_____
_____
_____
_____

insight learned:

_____
_____
_____
_____
_____

personalized verse, prayer, or specific project:

_____
_____
_____
_____
_____
_____
_____
_____
_____
_____
_____

⦁⦁ BOASTING TONGUE ⦁⦁

James 3:5

verse

_____
_____
_____
_____
_____

insight learned:

_____
_____
_____
_____
_____
_____

personalized verse, prayer, or specific project:

_____
_____
_____
_____
_____
_____
_____
_____
_____

∞∞ BRIDLED TONGUE ∞∞

James 1:26

verse

_____

_____

_____

_____

_____

insight learned:

_____

_____

_____

_____

_____

personalized verse, prayer, or specific project:

_____

_____

_____

_____

_____

_____

_____

_____

_____

_____

_____

⌾ CONFESSING TONGUE ⌾

Philippians 2:11

verse

_____

_____

_____

_____

_____

insight learned:

_____

_____

_____

_____

_____

_____

personalized verse, prayer, or specific project:

_____

_____

_____

_____

_____

_____

_____

_____

_____

_____

_____

∾ CONTROLLED TONGUE ∾
Proverbs 21:23

verse

_____
_____
_____
_____
_____

insight learned:

_____
_____
_____
_____
_____
_____

personalized verse, prayer, or specific project:

_____
_____
_____
_____
_____
_____
_____
_____
_____
_____
_____

ᴐᴐᴐ DECEITFUL TONGUE ᴐᴐᴐ

Psalm 120:2

verse

_____
_____
_____
_____
_____

insight learned:

_____
_____
_____
_____
_____
_____

personalized verse, prayer, or specific project:

_____
_____
_____
_____
_____
_____
_____
_____
_____
_____
_____
_____

∞ EVIL TONGUE ∞

Psalm 34:13

verse

_____

_____

_____

_____

_____

insight learned:

_____

_____

_____

_____

_____

_____

personalized verse, prayer, or specific project:

_____

_____

_____

_____

_____

_____

_____

_____

_____

_____

ᨀ FALSE TONGUE ᨀ
Psalm 120:3

verse

_____

_____

_____

_____

_____

insight learned:

_____

_____

_____

_____

_____

_____

personalized verse, prayer, or specific project:

_____

_____

_____

_____

_____

_____

_____

_____

_____

_____

_____

_____

∞ FIERY TONGUE ∞

James 3:6

verse

_____
_____
_____
_____
_____

insight learned:

_____
_____
_____
_____
_____
_____

personalized verse, prayer, or specific project:

_____
_____
_____
_____
_____
_____
_____
_____
_____
_____

∞ HEALING TONGUE ∞

Proverbs 12:18

verse

_____
_____
_____
_____
_____

insight learned:

_____
_____
_____
_____
_____

personalized verse, prayer, or specific project:

_____
_____
_____
_____
_____
_____
_____
_____
_____
_____
_____

∞ HELD (CONTROLLED) TONGUE ∞

Job 6:24

verse

_____
_____
_____
_____
_____

insight learned:

_____
_____
_____
_____
_____
_____

personalized verse, prayer, or specific project:

_____
_____
_____
_____
_____
_____
_____
_____
_____
_____
_____

☙ JUST TONGUE ❧
Proverbs 10:20

verse

_____

_____

_____

_____

_____

insight learned:

_____

_____

_____

_____

_____

_____

personalized verse, prayer, or specific project:

_____

_____

_____

_____

_____

_____

_____

_____

_____

_____

_____

_____

_____

⚬⚬⚬ KIND TONGUE ⚬⚬⚬
Proverbs 31:26

verse

_____
_____
_____
_____
_____

insight learned:

_____
_____
_____
_____
_____
_____

personalized verse, prayer, or specific project:

_____
_____
_____
_____
_____
_____
_____
_____
_____
_____
_____

⟀ LOOSED TONGUE ⟀

Luke 1:64

verse

_____
_____
_____
_____
_____

insight learned:

_____
_____
_____
_____
_____

personalized verse, prayer, or specific project:

_____
_____
_____
_____
_____
_____
_____
_____
_____

∂∂∂∂ NAUGHTY TONGUE ∂∂∂∂
Proverbs 17:4

verse

_____
_____
_____
_____
_____

insight learned:

_____
_____
_____
_____
_____
_____

personalized verse, prayer, or specific project:

_____
_____
_____
_____
_____
_____
_____
_____
_____
_____
_____

∞ PERVERSE TONGUE ∞
Proverbs 17:20

verse

_____
_____
_____
_____
_____

insight learned:

_____
_____
_____
_____
_____
_____

personalized verse, prayer, or specific project:

_____
_____
_____
_____
_____
_____
_____
_____
_____
_____

∞ POWERFUL TONGUE ∞

Proverbs 18:21

verse

_____
_____
_____
_____
_____

insight learned:

_____
_____
_____
_____
_____
_____

personalized verse, prayer, or specific project:

_____
_____
_____
_____
_____
_____
_____
_____
_____
_____
_____

∞ RAGING TONGUE ∞

Hosea 7:16

verse

_____
_____
_____
_____
_____

insight learned:

_____
_____
_____
_____
_____
_____

personalized verse, prayer, or specific project:

_____
_____
_____
_____
_____
_____
_____
_____
_____
_____

∞ SHARP TONGUE ∞
Psalm 57:4

verse

_____

_____

_____

_____

_____

insight learned:

_____

_____

_____

_____

_____

personalized verse, prayer, or specific project:

_____

_____

_____

_____

_____

_____

_____

_____

_____

_____

_____

∽⊗∽ SMITING TONGUE ∽⊗∽
Jeremiah 18:18

verse

_____

_____

_____

_____

_____

insight learned:

_____

_____

_____

_____

_____

_____

personalized verse, prayer, or specific project:

_____

_____

_____

_____

_____

_____

_____

_____

_____

_____

_____

∝∽ SOFT TONGUE ∽∝
Proverbs 25:15

verse

_____
_____
_____
_____
_____

insight learned:

_____
_____
_____
_____
_____

personalized verse, prayer, or specific project:

_____
_____
_____
_____
_____
_____
_____
_____
_____
_____

·◦◦◦ STAMMERING TONGUE ◦◦◦·

Isaiah 32:4, 33:19

verse

_____
_____
_____
_____
_____

insight learned:

_____
_____
_____
_____
_____

personalized verse, prayer, or specific project:

_____
_____
_____
_____
_____
_____
_____
_____
_____

⌇⌇ TRAINED TONGUE ⌇⌇

Jeremiah 9:5

verse

_____

_____

_____

_____

_____

insight learned:

_____

_____

_____

_____

_____

personalized verse, prayer, or specific project:

_____

_____

_____

_____

_____

_____

_____

_____

_____

_____

_____

⚬⚬⚬ UNTAMED TONGUE ⚬⚬⚬
James 3:8

verse

_____
_____
_____
_____
_____

insight learned:

_____
_____
_____
_____
_____
_____

personalized verse, prayer, or specific project:

_____
_____
_____
_____
_____
_____
_____
_____
_____
_____
_____
_____

MOUTH

WORDS OF WISDOM

ACCEPTABLE WORDS OF THE MOUTH

Psalm 19:14

verse

_____

_____

_____

_____

_____

insight learned:

_____

_____

_____

_____

_____

_____

personalized verse, prayer, or specific project:

_____

_____

_____

_____

_____

_____

_____

_____

_____

_____

_____

·ᗞᗞᗞ· MOUTH OF BLESSING ·ᗞᗞᗞ·

Psalm 34:1

verse

_____

_____

_____

_____

_____

insight learned:

_____

_____

_____

_____

_____

personalized verse, prayer, or specific project:

_____

_____

_____

_____

_____

_____

_____

_____

_____

_____

_____

∞ MOUTH THAT BLESSES & CURSES ∞
James 3:10

verse

_____

_____

_____

_____

_____

insight learned:

_____

_____

_____

_____

_____

personalized verse, prayer, or specific project:

_____

_____

_____

_____

_____

_____

_____

_____

_____

_____

_____

∞ BOLD MOUTH ∞

Ephesians 6:19

verse

_____
_____
_____
_____
_____

insight learned:

_____
_____
_____
_____
_____
_____

personalized verse, prayer, or specific project:

_____
_____
_____
_____
_____
_____
_____
_____
_____
_____
_____

∞ CONFESSING MOUTH ∞
Romans 10:9-10

verse

_____

_____

_____

_____

_____

insight learned:

_____

_____

_____

_____

_____

personalized verse, prayer, or specific project:

_____

_____

_____

_____

_____

_____

_____

_____

_____

_____

_____

✦ CRAVING MOUTH ✦
Proverbs 16:26

verse

_____
_____
_____
_____
_____

insight learned:

_____
_____
_____
_____
_____

personalized verse, prayer, or specific project:

_____
_____
_____
_____
_____
_____
_____
_____
_____

∂∅∅ MOUTH THAT DELIVERS ∅∅∂
Proverbs 12:6

verse

_____
_____
_____
_____
_____

insight learned:

_____
_____
_____
_____
_____
_____

personalized verse, prayer, or specific project:

_____
_____
_____
_____
_____
_____
_____
_____
_____
_____
_____

～ MOUTH THAT EDIFIES ～
Ephesians 4:29

verse

_____

_____

_____

_____

_____

insight learned:

_____

_____

_____

_____

_____

_____

personalized verse, prayer, or specific project:

_____

_____

_____

_____

_____

_____

_____

_____

_____

_____

_____

∞ EVIL MOUTH ∞
Proverbs 15:28

verse

_____
_____
_____
_____
_____

insight learned:

_____
_____
_____
_____
_____

personalized verse, prayer, or specific project:

_____
_____
_____
_____
_____
_____
_____
_____
_____
_____

∞ FROWARD MOUTH ∞
Proverbs 10:32

verse

_____
_____
_____
_____
_____

insight learned:

_____
_____
_____
_____
_____
_____

personalized verse, prayer, or specific project:

_____
_____
_____
_____
_____
_____
_____
_____
_____
_____
_____

∞ FRUITFUL MOUTH ∞
Proverbs 13:2, 18:20

verse

_____
_____
_____
_____
_____

insight learned:

_____
_____
_____
_____
_____
_____

personalized verse, prayer, or specific project:

_____
_____
_____
_____
_____
_____
_____
_____
_____
_____
_____

ᨆ HYPOCRITICAL MOUTH ᨆ
Proverbs 11:9

verse

_____
_____
_____
_____
_____
_____

insight learned:

_____
_____
_____
_____
_____
_____

personalized verse, prayer, or specific project:

_____
_____
_____
_____
_____
_____
_____
_____
_____
_____
_____

∞ REVEALING MOUTH ∞

Luke 6:45

verse

_____

_____

_____

_____

_____

insight learned:

_____

_____

_____

_____

_____

personalized verse, prayer, or specific project:

_____

_____

_____

_____

_____

_____

_____

_____

_____

_____

RIGHTEOUS MOUTH
Proverbs 8:8

verse

_____
_____
_____
_____
_____

insight learned:

_____
_____
_____
_____
_____
_____

personalized verse, prayer, or specific project:

_____
_____
_____
_____
_____
_____
_____
_____
_____
_____
_____

~ MOUTH SPEAKING SWELLING WORDS ~
Jude 1:16

verse

_____
_____
_____
_____
_____

insight learned:

_____
_____
_____
_____
_____
_____

personalized verse, prayer, or specific project:

_____
_____
_____
_____
_____
_____
_____
_____
_____
_____
_____
_____

∞ VIOLENT MOUTH ∞
Proverbs 10:6, 11

verse

_____
_____
_____
_____
_____

insight learned:

_____
_____
_____
_____
_____
_____

personalized verse, prayer, or specific project:

_____
_____
_____
_____
_____
_____
_____
_____
_____
_____

‹‹‹›› MOUTH THAT'S A WELL OF LIFE ‹‹‹››
Proverbs 10:11

verse
_____
_____
_____
_____
_____

insight learned:
_____
_____
_____
_____
_____

personalized verse, prayer, or specific project:
_____
_____
_____
_____
_____
_____
_____
_____
_____

A WELLSPRING OF WISDOM
Proverbs 18:4

verse

_____
_____
_____
_____
_____

insight learned:

_____
_____
_____
_____
_____

personalized verse, prayer, or specific project:

_____
_____
_____
_____
_____
_____
_____
_____
_____
_____

Resources available from
THE LEARNING PARENT

CHARACTER CONCEPTS CURRICULUM
LEVEL 5 • AGES 8–13

Growing in Wisdom

• **Study 32 types of negative behavior and their consequences.**

• Learn how to make an intentional decision to choose positive, godly character.

• Every negative character quality is just a positive one misused. This study guides your child in learning to make wise decisions based on God's Word.

CHARACTER CONCEPTS CURRICULUM
LEVEL 6 • AGES 13–15

Living the Fruitful Life

• **Learn how to apply the fruits of the Spirit to your daily life.**

• Practical Bible study that teaches young people to search out insights from God's Word for themselves.

Power in Proverbs

- Exciting new self-study guide to help your teenager take advantage of the matchless wisdom contained in the book of Proverbs!
- This study teaches your teen how to use the concordance and his Bible to search the Scripture on topics applicable to everyday life.
- Includes two sets of practically applied flashcards from the Book of Wisdom

Proverbs People Collection

Proverbs People Collection features Proverbs People workbooks I and II, our most popular products for children aged seven to twelve. In addition, it includes Proverbs People flashcards, providing two Bible verses for each character type presented in theProverbs People workbooks. The collection also features the 5-cd set, Uncle Rick Reads the Proverbs. Your children will hear Uncle Rick read and explain the entire book of Proverbs. They will memorize God's word effortlessly by listening!

The Workbooks are chock-full of short-answer questions, example stories, fun quizzes, application questions, and coloring pages teaching the character type in Proverbs.

Book 1 teaches the following character qualities:
"Righteous/Wicked"
"The Five Fools"
"The Prudent Man"
"The Wise Man"
"Liar/Faithful Witness"

Book 2 Includes:
Teaches the following character traits:
"Virtuous Woman vs. Contentious Woman"
"Proud vs. Humble"
"Fearful vs. Trusting"
"Angry Man vs. Patient Man"
"Content vs. Covetous"
"Cruel vs. Merciful"
"Flatterer vs. Honest"

Help your child experience the power of Scripture through character study and reinforced listening as well!

All resources available at www.CharacterConcepts.com

Resources available from
THE LEARNING PARENT

CHARACTER CONCEPTS CURRICULUM
LEVEL 9 • AGES HIGH SCHOOL–ADULT

For You They Signed

FOR YOU THEY SIGNED curriculum can be used with high schoolers to teach them history and character at the same time. It is crucial that we arm our young people with the truth about the founders who started this great nation.

In 1776, 56 men signed their names on a document that they knew might well mean their certain deaths as traitors to England. Standing on principles of faith and liberty, these men forged a powerful call for freedom and human dignity still resonating today in America. Yet, historical revisionists have distorted or attempted to wipe away every trace of this nation's Christian heritage, including the heartfelt faith of these founding fathers.

More than simply facts and figures, FOR YOU THEY SIGNED provides an abundance of resources within one volume, including over 90 illustrations, biographical summaries, and insightful quotes, character quality definitions, Patrick Henry`s speech delivered to the signers, the Christian nature of state constitutions, and the Christian nature of America`s universities. Thought-provoking questions are supplied within the text to help your young people retain what they are learning.

The Declaration of Independence remains one of history's most enduring achievements, and this text will help your young person learn to value those freedoms these men fought for in an insightfully fresh way. It will also assist you in catching the God-given vision of these faithful new Americans, igniting a fire for your family for generations to come! Here is a volume that should be found in every private and public library in America . . . a meticulously documented look back to the true birth of our nation.

They pledged their lives, their fortunes, and their sacred honor so we could be free!

Endorsed by Christian historian David Barton of Wallbuilders! This beautiful volume gives you the tools you need to train up young nation-changers.

Can be used by junior high through adults or as a family together! FOR YOU THEY SIGNED CURRICULUM includes hard cover book, downloadable activity book, and flashcards of the signers with Scripture verses. A year's worth of history and character studies!

Curriculum comes with a set of flashcards—one for each of the 56 signers of the Declararation of Independence. Your young person will learn what each signer looked like, as well as which character quality his life exemplified and a Bible verse to learn as well. What a great way to retain information you are learning in FOR YOU THEY SIGNED!